Early Activities

KU-350-774

counting

Educational adviser: Alison Shelley
Illustrator: Sue Harris
Series editor: Peter Nicholls

Published by James Galt & Co. Ltd., Sovereign House, Stockport Road, Cheadle, Cheshire, SK8 2EA, England.

Printed in China.

ISBN 0-903004-21-6

Matching

Can you find the umbrella sticker?

Can you draw a handle for each umbrella?

Is there a hat for everyone?
Draw lines to help you.

Sorting Out

Draw a ring around each group of bugs that are the same.

Can you find the balloon sticker?

Now colour the big balloons blue
and the small ones yellow.

3

one

How many fire engines can you count?

 **2**   **3**   4   5   **6**   7   **8**   9   **10**

Find the number

How many houses can you count?

Can you draw a tail on the cow?

Draw one flower in the frame.
Now colour it.

4

How many hot air balloons can you count?

Find the number

 3 4 5 6 7 8 9 10

Can you count the pigs?

Here are 2 ice creams.

Can you draw 2 lollipops?

Draw 2 eyes and a nose on the clown.

three

How many dogs can you count?

Find the number

1 2 3 4 5 6 7 8 9 10

Count the flowers.

Can you draw 2 more balls?

---------- ----------

How many balls are there now?

How many birds are in each set? Join the sets to the right numbers.

6

four

How many dinosaurs can you count?

Find the number

1 2 3 4 5 6 7 8 9 10

Count the birds.

Colour by numbers

1 blue
2 green
3 yellow
4 red

five

Find the number

How many robots can you count?

| | | | | | 6 | 7 | 8 | 9 | 10 |

Can you count the sweets?

Draw 5 candles on the cake.

How old are you?

I am ◯ years old.

6
six

Find the number

How many fish can you count?

1 2 3 4 5 6   7   8   9   10

Say the numbers on the train.

How many ducks are there in each picture?

ducks

ducks

There are the same number of ducks in each picture.

seven

How many colours are there in the rainbow?

Find the number

8   9   10

Can you count the elephants?

Count the apples and colour them in.

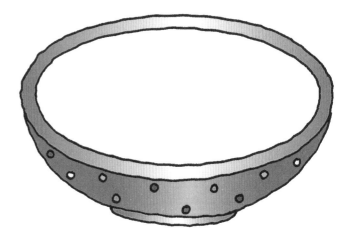

Draw 7 oranges in the bowl.

10

eight

Find the number

How many octopuses can you count?

1 2 3 4 5 6 7 8 9 10

How many legs do spiders have?
Count them and then colour in this picture.

Now draw 8 legs on this spider.

nine

How many cats can you count?

Find the number

10

Can you count the cars and trucks in the traffic jam?

How many blue spots can you count on the dog?

Can you draw 9 spots on this dog?

There are  blue spots.

10

ten

Find the number

How many teddies can you count?

Can you count the clothes on the washing line?

Help Bobby Bear find his way home by joining the numbers in order.

Writing Numbers 1 to 5

First trace the numbers with your finger. Then use the dotted lines to help you. Now you can try writing the numbers on your own.

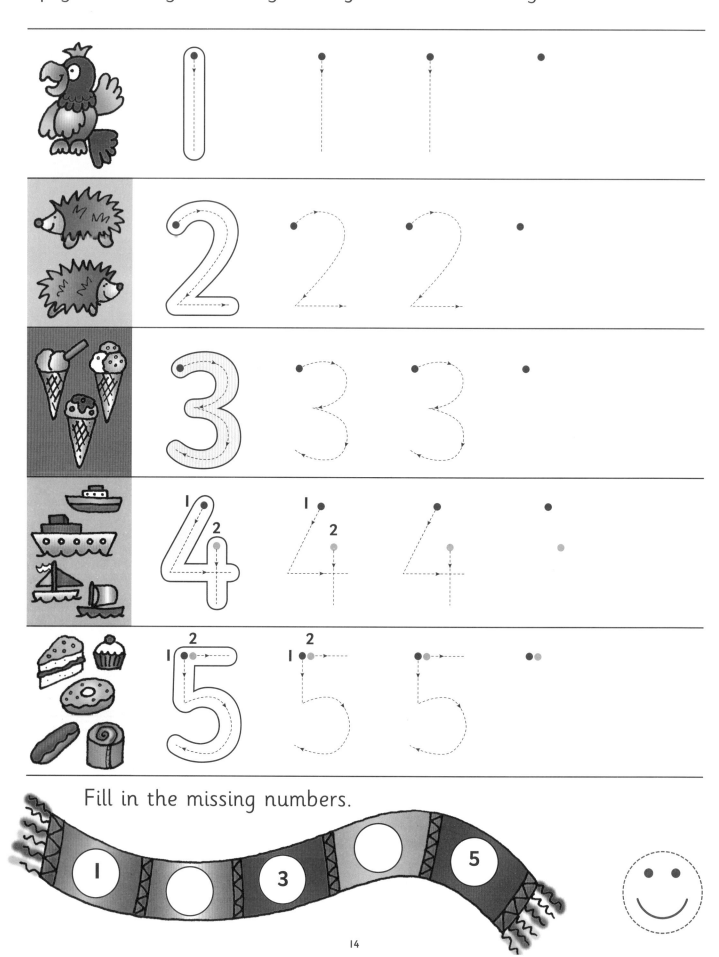

Fill in the missing numbers.

Writing Numbers 6 to 10

First trace the numbers with your finger. Then use the dotted lines to help you. Now you can try writing the numbers on your own.

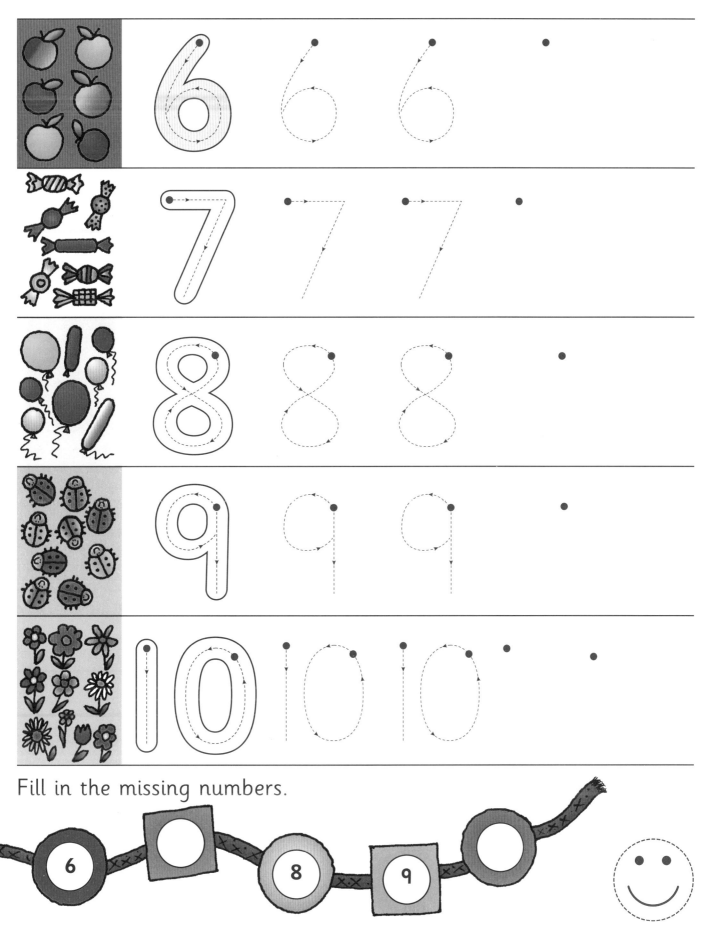

Fill in the missing numbers.

Toy Shop Counting

Look carefully at the picture.

Count these toys in the toy shop. Fill in the answer boxes.

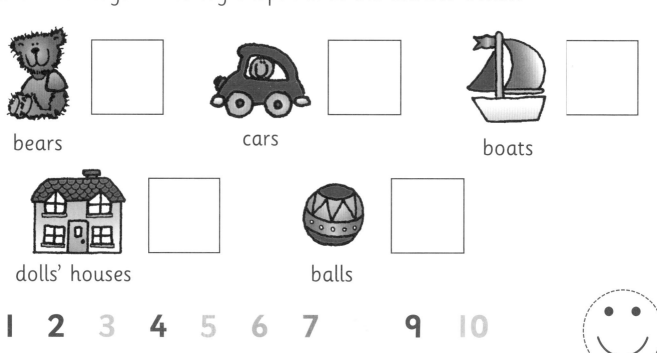

bears

cars

boats

dolls' houses

balls

1 2 3 **4** 5 6 **7** **9** 10

zero

Find the number

How many elephants can you count?

3 birds

2 birds

1 bird

0 birds

Give each teddy a cake. Draw lines to help you.

How many cakes are left?

Missing Numbers

Can you fill in the missing numbers?

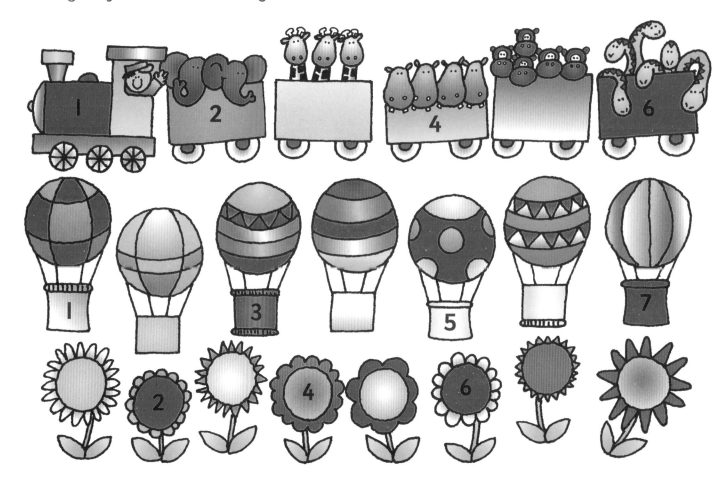

Find the sticker and see if you can fill in the missing numbers.

1 2 3 **4** 5 6 **7** **9** 10

How many can you count?

Count the fish in each bowl and draw a ring around the right number.

2   3   **4**   6   **7**

How many people are in each bus?

3   **4**   5   7   **9**

How many birds are in each nest?

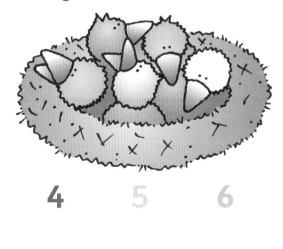 

4   5   **6**   **0**   **I**   **2**

0 **I** **2** 3 **4** 5 **6** **7**   **9** 10

Spot the Difference

Can you find 8 things that are missing in the bottom picture?

Draw a ring around them in the top picture.

I 2 3 4 5 6 7   9 10

One More

Draw **1** more and count. How many are there now?

_____ [ ] cakes

_____ [ ] sweets

_____ [ ] lollipops

Two More

Draw **2** more and count. How many are there now?

_____ [ ] presents

_____ [ ] kites

_____ [ ] balls

1 2 3 4 5 6 7 8 9 10

Dot to Dot

Who is hiding in the picture? Join the numbers in the right order to find out. Then find the sticker for this page.

Count these creatures in the big picture. Fill in the boxes.

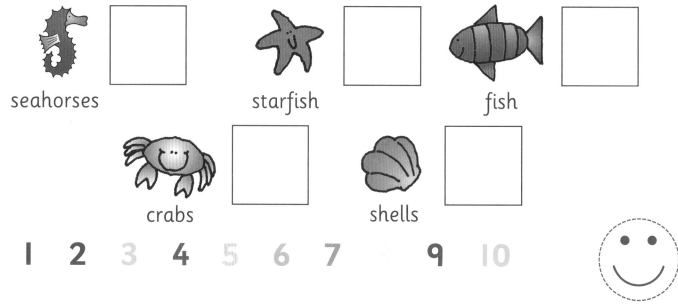

seahorses   starfish   fish

crabs   shells

1 2 3 4 5 6 7 9 10

Counting Down

Can you count down? Start at **10** and say each number down to **1** then we have lift off!

ten
nine
eight
seven
six
five
four
three
two
one

lift off!

10
9
8
7
6
5
4
3
2
1

lift off!

One Less

Here are **5** penguins. **1** goes for a swim. How many are left?

Here are **7** balloons. **1** balloon pops. How many are left?

Here are **3** apples. You eat **1** apple. How many are left?

1 2 3 4 5 6 7 9 10

Treasure Hunt Maze

Pirate Pete has lost his treasure. Join the numbers in the right order to help him through the maze.

Well done!

Give yourself the special star sticker for all your good work.